TOMORROW'S KITCHEN

ILLUSTRATED BY SHUANGSHUANG HAO
EDITED BY DEBORAH MAY

First published in Scotland in 2020 by
Kitchen Press
1 Windsor Place
Dundee, DD2 1BG

Illustration © Shuangshuang Hao 2020
shuangshuanghao.com

Text © Deborah May, Kerry Hudson, Emma Brown, Sonia Michalewicz,
Andrés Blanco, Yasmine Sefraoui, Sara Shaarawi, Asiimwe Deborah
Kawe, Ery Nzaramba, Lubna Said Alhajjar, Saubia Safdar,
Kirsty Gibson, Sumayya Usmani, Shazia, Rebecca Tantony,
Katie Catling 2020.

Text design by Andrew Forteath
andrewforteath.co.uk

A CIP record for this book is available from the British Library.

ISBN: 978-1-9163165-0-8
Printed in India

INTRODUCTION

Tomorrow's Kitchen began as a series of events which took place within Festival 2018, the arts and culture engagement programme that ran alongside the European Championships in Glasgow.

Inspired by the mix of cultural influences in dishes from Glasgow's Haggis Pakora, the Californian sushi roll, Durban's Bunny Chow, Peranakan cuisine in Indonesia and more, the Tomorrow's Kitchen events looked to be creative and curious, exploring the idea of 'Scottish' cuisine in an increasingly multicultural Glasgow. We wanted to invent new recipes while asking the question – what could our current and traditional cuisine look like in the future as the city diversifies?

As Founder and Director of the food-led social business Küche – 'A Multicultural Kitchen For All' which collaborates with a collective of cooks navigating the UK immigration system, we commissioned Syrian, Pakistani, Iraqi, Roma and two Scottish cooks to invent a collection of new recipes. Some of the recipes they created are included here, including Cullen Skink Dumplings, Spiced Tattie Scones and Neep Gobi. Other recipes (Baklava Pancakes, Persian Porridge and Roma Polenta Poutine) came from ideas dreamt up by participants who attended the Tomorrow's Kitchen events when we asked them to invent a dish, a dish that the world had never tasted before and which might be inspired by a memory, mood, story, culture, object, anything at all. Cooks Yasmine Sefraoui, Kirsty Gibson and Emma Brown then did the amazing work of turning these ideas into real – and delicious – recipes.

A graphic novel cookbook authored by the community was an idea that developed from this series of events, and like so many ideas it came from a web of different experiences and conversations. The idea came from reading Alison Bechdel's *Fun Home*, Art Spiegelman's *Maus* and Shaun Tan's *The Arrival* – I fell in love with graphic novels during my study of Comparative Literature at university.

The idea came from my love of books and a long-standing personal ambition to publish one myself. The idea came from my desire for Küche to be about many different artforms, and to involve people from across the world, both the diaspora community living in Scotland and also people living their lives across other continents. The idea came from Küche's social mission to open up conversations, counteract negative attitudes, and provide opportunities for people to be more socially and culturally informed and react responsibly and with empathy to our wider world. The idea – like so many ideas – came out of creativity, curiosity and conversation.

Tomorrow's Kitchen became an opportunity to reconnect and document some of the incredible voices from around the world I have had the opportunity to listen to; voices that tell both personal and collective stories, that share important ideas and experiences on politics, poverty, history, religion, borders, grief, gender and more. These voices include Rwandan playwright Ery Nzaramba, whose brilliant play *Split/Mixed* was the subject of my University dissertation 5 years ago; Ugandan playwright Deborah Asiimwe who I did an internship with as she created Kampala's first ever international theatre festival; Lubna who lives in Gaza and wrote to Küche a year ago asking for work – we couldn't give her regular employment but we did invite her to contribute to Tomorrow's Kitchen, across countries, seas and inhuman regimes; Andrés Blanco who came to Küche's Venezuelan event last year and who generously spoke about politics and shared his ideas and experience with us; Katie Catling, a dear friend of mine who lost her mother two years ago and who shares a slice of her grief with us; writer Kerry Hudson who spoke at the Homeless World Cup on 'Unlocking the stories that can tackle poverty and homelessness', who I wrote an article on as a volunteer writer; poet Rebecca Tantony who I saw lead a creative writing workshop to a room of teenagers on poetry and recipe making at a school in Swindon for the creative writing charity I worked for at the time, First Story; Shazia who shared her story about our belly buttons at a creative workshop Küche co-hosted in Glasgow for people navigating the UK immigration system; Sara Shaarawi, a playwright whose political, funny and multilingual work I have heard snippets of across Glasgow's stages; Sumayya Usmani whose delicious fusion food I tasted at a Burns Supper years ago, a 'Scottistani' meal which I will always remember. These are the Tomorrow's Kitchen contributors who I made contact with last year, asking them to share some kind of experience through the medium of food.

Unlike the other contributors, I didn't find the illustrator for this project through an experience or conversation. I found Shuangshuang Hao through a random Google search. The role was so key to the success of the book that I wanted to work with someone with lived experience of migration, who would interpret the contributors' stories ethically and empathetically. I was also hoping to find someone who came from a different part of the world, but who had experience of Glasgow in some capacity. I was delighted to discover Shuangshuang. Shuangshuang lives in Shanghai but studied at Glasgow School of Art for one year. She is an artist who was nominated for a Scottish BAFTA but who was refused a visa and was unable to continue her studies here. Most important, perhaps, was her personal love and experience of working with the comic book form. What struck me about Shuangshuang's work was her ability to work in so many different styles, how her artwork looked as though it was the work of tens of different illustrators, not just the work of one: a skill which gives each story in this book its own visual interpretation.

Tomorrow's Kitchen's mission is to use food and illustration to describe experiences that make us understand a little more about humanity and the wider world around us. It amplifies a collection of unique voices, voices which challenge us and make us think as readers and cooks through recipes, illustrations and stories.

I want to give thanks to our funders National Lottery's Awards For All and Glasgow City Council's Arts Development Scheme as well as our publishers Kitchen Press for making this project and publication possible. I want to give thanks to the incredible voices and drawings which have ultimately brought 'Tomorrow's Kitchen' to life and made it the beautiful book which I hope you will look at and think about today and re-look and re-think about tomorrow and the next day and the next…

DEBORAH MAY

MINCE, TATTIES AND SKIRLIE

STORY BY KERRY HUDSON

FAMILIES ARE COMPLICATED BUT FOOD, FOR ME, HAS ALWAYS BEEN SIMPLE.

A LOVE OF THE WARMTH AND FRAGRANCE OF A POT ON THE COOKER TOP, OF EATING, OF A FULL BELLY.

AND THE SLOW FEELING THAT COMES WITH IT ARE PLEASURES THAT THE COMPLICATED WOMEN OF MY FAMILY PASSED DOWN TO EACH OTHER WHEN THEY HAD DIFFICULTY COMMUNICATING OTHERWISE.

THE MATERNAL SIDE OF MY FAMILY ARE FROM ABERDEEN IN SCOTLAND, A FISHING TOWN THAT BECAME AN OIL CITY, WHERE MONEY ROLLED IN BUT NOT FOR THE ENCLAVE OF TORRY WHERE I GREW UP.

NOT FOR THOSE WHO'D DEPENDED ON THE FISHING TRADE FOR GENERATIONS.

MY GRANDMA, MY MOTHER, MY AUNTS AND GREAT AUNTS WORKED IN PROCESSING - FILLETING AND PACKING THE COMMERCIALLY CAUGHT FISH IN FREEZING TEMPERATURES IN DESOLATE BUILDINGS ON THE EDGE OF TOWN. THEY WERE FISH FACTORIES BUT THEY CALL THEM 'FISH HOOSES',

AND CALL THEMSELVES 'FISH WIVES'.

WHICH ALWAYS MADE ME THINK OF THEM, IN LAYERS OF CARDIGANS AND HEADSCARFS, GOSSIPING AROUND A TABLE WITH CHIPPED MUGS OF TEA AT THEIR ELBOWS.

THIS WAS TRUE OF THE EARLIER GENERATIONS, THE WOMEN WHO MENDED NETS ON THE SHORES OF THE DOCKS.

WHO TRAVELLED THE LENGTH OF BRITAIN CHASING SHOALS OF HERRING.

WHO WERE SO POOR THEY WERE NICKNAMED 'RYAN SEAGULLS' BECAUSE THEY WERE ALWAYS ROAMING, ALWAYS SCAVENGING FOR FOOD OR A LUMP OF COAL.

NO MATTER THE AESTHETIC MY MIND CONJURED, WHAT NEVER CHANGED WAS THAT THESE WOMEN HAD HARD, HARD LIVES.

FISH WIVES WERE NOTORIOUSLY STRONG AND FIERCE, TOUGHER THAN THEIR FISHER-MEN HUSBANDS. IF THEY WERE LUCKY ENOUGH TO HAVE A HUSBAND WHO WORKED.

MY CHILDHOOD WAS FULL OF STORIES OF FISHWIFE COMPETITIVENESS AND CAMARADERIE IN EQUAL MEASURES

A FILLETING KNIFE BEING HELD TO RIVALS' THROATS.

FISH AND CHIP SUPPERS SHARED FROM WARMED-THROUGH PAPER WRAPPERS ON PAY DAY IN THE SMALL DARK ROOM THAT STILL HAD THE METAL SMELL OF FISH BLOOD.

THERE WAS NO MONEY.

THERE WERE A LOT OF CHILDREN.

THERE WERE OFTEN HUSBANDS WHO WERE AWAY OR, INDEED, HUSBANDS WHO THE WOMEN WOULD WISH WOULD GO AWAY.

[T]HERE WAS LITTLE TIME AND FEW CHOICES.

BUT ON SUNDAY THERE WAS ALWAYS MINCE, TATTIES AND SKIRLIE. WARM, CHEAP, FILLING AND DELICIOUS.

[E]ACH SUNDAY AFTERNOON THE AIR WOULD BE CLOAKED IN THE [S]MELL OF FRYING MEAT AND ONION WHILE THE TV THREW [L]IGHT AND WORDS ACROSS THE CRAMPED LIVING ROOM.

AND FINALLY, THOSE WOMEN RELAXED.

[I] MADE A DIFFERENT [S]ORT OF LIFE FOR [M]YSELF, BUT THIS [I]S A RECIPE I TOOK [W]ITH ME.

A TRIBUTE TO THE HEALING, JOYFUL SIMPLICITY A PLATE OF GOOD FOOD WHEN TIMES ARE DIFFICULT OR TIRING.

MINCE, TATTIES AND SKIRLIE
A WARMING RECIPE FOR COLD DAYS AND HARD WORK.

250g MINCE

SALT & PEPPER TO TASTE

2 ONIONS

2 CLOVES OF GARLIC MINCED (NOT TRADITIONAL BUT GARLIC IS A GOOD THING.)

2 CARROTS

1 TABLESPOON OF MARMITE (AGAIN, NOT TRADITION BUT A GOOD THING.)

500ML OF BEEF STOCK

3 LARGE POTATOES

2 TABLESPOONS OF OIL

1/2 CUP OF MILK

100g OF OATMEAL

3 TABLESPOONS OF BUTTER

FINELY CHOP ONE ONION AND THE CARROTS. USING SOME OF THE OIL, SOFTEN IN A PAN ALONG WITH THE MINCED GARLIC.

ADD THE MINCE AND COOK UNTIL BROWNED.

STIR IN THE STOCK, MARMITE AND A LIBERAL AMOUNT OF PEPPER, LEAVE TO SIMMER ON A LOW HEAT UNTIL THE SAUCE HAS THICKENED AND THE HOUSE SMELLS LIKE SUNDAY AFTERNOONS IN ABERDEEN.

PEEL AND CUT POTATOES INTO QUARTERS.

BOIL UNTIL A FORK CAN GO THROUGH THEM AND DRAIN.

MASH WITH BUTTER, MILK, AND PEPPER TO TASTE AND KEEP WARM ON A VERY LOW HEAT.

INELY CHOP THE REMAINING ONION ND FRY IN BUTTER.

ADD THE OATMEAL, FRY FOR 5 MINUTES OR SO OR UNTIL THE OATMEAL IS COATED IN BUTTER AND TASTES COOKED. SEASON WITH SALT AND PEPPER.

DISH UP!

EAT LARGE PORTIONS, MAYBE HAVE A GLASS OF COLD DARK BEER, GO BACK FOR SECONDS, HAVE A NAP AFTERWARDS AND ENJOY YOUR DAY OF REST BECAUSE YOU'VE EARNED IT.

CULLEN SKINK-INSPIRED KIPPER DUMPLINGS WITH CHEESE SAUCE

BY EMMA BROWN AND SONIA MICHALEWICZ

SERVES 4

INGREDIENTS FOR KIPPER DUMPLINGS

500g FLOUR

2 EGGS

300ml WATER

1 SMOKED KIPPER FILLET, FLAKED.

100g POTATO COOKED AND MASHED

30g LEEK, DICED

30g ONION, DICED

SALT AND PEPPER TO SEASON

2-3 TSP CRÈME FRAÎCHE. ENOUGH TO BIND TOGETHER

A FEW SPRIGS FRESH PARSLEY, CHOPPED.

20g BUTTER

20g PLAIN FLOUR

300ml MILK

20g ONION · DICED

2 SPRING ONIONS. CHOPPED

WHITE PEPPER

20g MILD SCOTTISH CHEESE, GRATED

1 TSP OIL

FEW SPRIGS FRESH PARSLEY, CHOPPED

SIFT THE FLOUR INTO A BOWL
AND ADD THE EGGS. MAKE THE
DOUGH BY POURING IN WATER
AND STIRRING VERY SLOWLY.

DIVIDE DOUGH INTO TWO AND
COVER BOTH WITH A DAMP
CLOTH.

PLACE THE DICED ONION AND
LEEK IN A FRYING PAN WITH
SOME BUTTER OVER MEDIUM
HEAT AND SWEAT UNTIL SOFT.

IN A BOWL, COMBINE THE KIPPER,
POTATO, CRÈME FRAÎCHE, PARSLEY
WITH THE LEEK AND ONION MIXTURE.
MIX UNTIL COMBINED. SEASON WITH
SALT AND PLENTY OF PEPPER.

ROLL OUT THE DOUGH TO A THICK-
NESS OF 2 CM, CUT DISCS WITH A
GLASS OR A SPECIAL MOULD. PLACE
A SPOON OF FILLING ON EACH DISC.
FOLD IN HALF AND CAREFULLY SEAL
TO ENSURE THE FILLING WON'T ESCAPE.
TIGHTEN WITH A FORK CREATING
A FRILL.

COOK IN BATCHES IN BOILING,
SALTED WATER. WHEN DUMPL-
INGS FLOAT TO THE TOP REMOVE
CAREFULLY WITH A SLOTTED
SPOON.

FOR THE SAUCE, PLACE THE BUTTER
AND OIL IN A SAUCEPAN OVER A
MEDIUM HEAT. ONCE MELTED, FRY
THE ONION UNTIL SOFT AND THEN
ADD IN THE SPRING ONIONS.

ON A LOW HEAT STIR IN THE
FLOUR FOR ONE MINUTE TO
ENSURE IT DOESN'T HAVE A
FLOURY TEXTURE.

ADD THE MILK A LITTLE AT A
TIME, CONSTANTLY WHISKING
AFTER EACH ADDITION UNTIL
SMOOTH. KEEP ADDING UNTIL
YOU HAVE USED ALL THE MILK.
YOU SHOULD HAVE A SMOOTH,
CREAMY CONSISTENCY.

ADD IN THE CHESE AND STIR IN
UNTIL MELTED.

TO FINISH. ADD IN THE PEPPER
AND PARSLEY AND SERVE WITH
THE DUMPLING.

LA CANGREJADA

STORY BY ANDRÉS BLANCO

CHAPTER 1

THE BEGINNING

JULIETA WAS A VERY STRONG WEE WOMAN FROM SORO, ON THE SOUTH COAST OF THE 'PENINSULA DE PARIA'.

SHE WAS WELL KNOWN IN TOWN FOR HER ABILITY TO FARM.

TO SWIM,

AND ESPECIALLY FOR HER COOKING.

WITH HER TINY WEE BODY, SHE WOULD SWIM THE GULF OF PARIA FIGHTING AGAINST SHARKS AND GIANT OCTOPUS TO GET TO TRINIDAD AND TOBAGO.

SHE NORMALLY WOULD MAKE SEVERAL TRIPS DURING THE YEAR TO GET DELICIOUS SPICES AND INGREDIENTS THAT SHE COULDN'T FIND IN HER HOMETOWN.

ON ONE OF HER TRIPS, SHE ENCOUNTERED THE CHIEF WOMAN OF A TRIBE WHO INVITED HER TO A SPECIAL DINNER.

THE MEN OF THE TRIBE SAT AROUND THE FIRE IN A CIRCLE. THE WOMEN WOULD BRING LARGE SAUCEPANS FULL OF CRABS TO BE COOKED.

ONCE THE MEN HAD FINISHED, THE REST OF THE FAMILY AND FRIENDS SAT AND ATE TOGETHER IN FRONT OF THE FIRE.

CHANTING AND GRATEFUL FOR THE FEAST.

JULIETA FELT SO MUCH LOVE FOR WHAT SHE SAW, SO SHE TRIED HER BEST TO REMEMBER ...

THE SMELL AND BLEND OF FLAVOURS.

THE SPICES AND THE COLOURS.

THOSE DAYS IT WAS DISRESPECTFUL TO ASK SOMEONE FOR THEIR COOKING SECRETS.

BUT JULIETA KNEW THAT THE MOST IMPORTANT INGREDIENT WAS THE CRABS.

SO SHE ORDERED A GREAT BOX OF CRABS AND SWAM WITH IT BACK TO SORO.

AT HOME SHE TESTED AND TASTED AND MADE SURE THAT HER DAUGHTERS LEARNT THE SECRET RECIPE TOO.

ONE OF THEM, DELIA, PAID PARTICULAR ATTENTION TO THE PROCESS.

CHAPTER 2

THE CAPITAL

DELIA - 'LA CATIRA' (THE GIRL WITH BLONDE HAIR) WAS MADLY IN LOVE WITH A VERY INTELLIGENT YOUNG AFRO-AMERICAN GUY FROM LA GUAIRA. SO IN LOVE THAT THEY VERY QUICKLY GOT MARRIED AND CREATED THEIR HOME IN CARACAS, THE CAPITAL OF VENEZUELA. THE FAMILY GREW AND GREW.

DELIA, LIKE HER MUM, COOKED FROM THE HEART.

SHE TRIED HARD TO MASTER THE CRAB RECIPE PASSED ON TO HER BY JULIETA.

SHE TRIED AND TASTED, TRIED AND TASTED, AND TRIED AND TASTED AGAIN. SHE FOUND OUT THE BEST CRAB FOR THE RECIPE WAS THE GIANT BLUE RIVER CRAB FOUND IN THE WATERS FAR AWAY.

FROM HERE ON THE EATING OF THE CRAB BECAME A FAMILY TRADITION AND WAS FORMALLY TITLED 'LA CANGREJADA'. THE CRAB FEAST.

CHAPTER 3

THE BLUE MONSTER

THE CRABS WERE FISHED FROM THE BIG RIVER FARAWAY BY MY GRANNY DELIA.

SHE WOULD BRING THEM HOME ALIVE AND KEEP THEM IN A LARGE BATHROOM IN THE BACK GARDEN OF MY GRANDPARENT'S HOUSE.

THEY WERE INITIALLY VERY WEE.

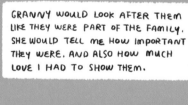

GRANNY WOULD LOOK AFTER THEM LIKE THEY WERE PART OF THE FAMILY. SHE WOULD TELL ME HOW IMPORTANT THEY WERE, AND ALSO HOW MUCH LOVE I HAD TO SHOW THEM.

TO START WITH IT WAS SCARY FOR ME BUT THEN I BEGAN TO ENJOY FEEDING AND BATHING THEM A COUPLE OF TIMES A WEEK.

19

UNTIL ONE DAY I GOT BACK FROM HOLIDAYS. AND THEY WERE— *HUUUUUUGE!*

THEY WERE A STRANGE BLUE COLOUR, WITH BIG EVIL EYES, EVEN MORE FRIGHTENING WERE THEIR EXTRA SHARP CLAWS.

SHARPER THAN A JAPANESE SWORD, AND BIGGER THAN THE CRAB ITSELF.

THEY WERE NOT FRIENDLY—LOOKING ANYMORE.

HOWEVER, FOR MY GRANNY, THEY LOOKED PERFECT AS THEY WERE NOW BIG ENOUGH FOR THE FEAST.

CHAPTER 4

THE BATTLEFIELD

FAMILY AND FRIENDS WOULD GATHER TOGETHER AT MY GRANDPARENTS' HOUSE.
I REMEMBER THE HOUSE TO BE MASSIVE WITH A LOT OF OUTSIDE SPACES.

I REMEMBER THE HOUSE FULL OF PEOPLE – ALL STARVING AND DESPERATE FOR THE FEAST TO BEGIN.

YOU COULD SENSE THEIR ANXIETY AND NERVOUSNESS AS THEY WAITED FOR THE FOOD TO ARRIVE.

EVERYONE WOULD SIT AROUND A VERY LARGE TABLE.

THE 'RED SAUCE' WOULD BE SERVED FIRST.

MADE OF STIR-FRIED SHALLOTS, GARLIC, COCONUT MILK, ANNATTO (NATURAL RED FOOD COLOUR LIKE SAFFRON), TARO (A TUBER IN THE SAME FAMILY AS CASSAVA AND YUCCA), AND SOME WHITE FISH MEAT.

EVERYONE WAS SWEATING AND AGITATED. THE ANTICIPATION MAKING THEM MORE AND MORE ANXIOUS AS THEY WAITED.

THEN THE MASHED GREEN AND PLANTAIN DONUTS WOULD BE SERVED.

FINALLY, WHAT EVERYONE WAS WAITING FOR. LARGE POTS FILLED WITH THE FRESHLY BOILED BLUE MONSTERS WERE PUT ON THE TABLE.

YOU COULD SEE PEOPLE JUMPING QUICKLY TO GRAB THE CRABS. RED SAUCE SPLASHED EVERYWHERE.

ALL YOU COULD HEAR WAS THE SOUND OF SHELLS CRACKING.

AND PEOPLE SHOUTING WITH THEIR MOUTHS RED LIKE ZOMBIES.

I WOULD SIT FAR AWAY FROM THEM, FRIGHTENED.

FOR ME, AT 8 YEARS OLD, IT RESEMBLED A BATTLEFIELD, A BATTLEFIELD FOR CRABS.

BUT IN REALITY THEY WERE JUST SHOWING AN ENORMOUS LOVE FOR THE FAMILY TRADITION - LA CANGREJADA - THE CRAB FEAST.

CHAPTER 5

SCOTLAND, THE REBORN ANGUS MCWHITE

THE POLITICAL AND ECONOMIC SITUATION IN VENEZUELA GOT WORSE. THERE WAS VIOLENCE, A LACK OF ALL BASIC SERVICES, A SHORTAGE OF FOOD AND MEDICINE, AND WORST OF ALL, A HOSTILE DICTATORSHIP RESPONSIBLE FOR THE MOST HORRIBLE BLOODSHED.

I DECIDED TO PURSUE A NEW HORIZON.

UNLIKE MY GREAT GRANNY I DIDN'T SWIM ACROSS THE SEA TO GET TO BONNY SCOTLAND BUT I DID HAVE TO FIGHT AGAINST BIG MONSTERS.

VISAS, VISAS, AND MORE VISAS.

JUST ANOTHER NUMBER IN THE IMMIGRATION SYSTEM.

UK VI

BUT IT WAS WORTH IT.

I AM NOW SETTLED, IN LOVE, AND FOREVER THANKFUL TO SCOTLAND, MY HOME. MY FRIENDS HAVE RENAMED ME, FROM ANDRES BLANCO, TO 'ANGUS MCWHITE'.

SADLY, BECAUSE OF MY FEAR OF THE BATTLEFIELD AND THE CRAB WAR, I NEVER TRIED MY GRANNY'S CRAB RECIPE.

I TRIED CRAB FOR THE FIRST TIME WHEN I MOVED TO SCOTLAND.

I'M TRYING TO MAKE CRABS!

SPECIFICALLY, IN NORTH BERWICK.

TASTING CRAB MADE ME REMEMBER THIS STORY. I REALISED THAT MY FAMILY GENES WERE KICKING IN AND THAT I WAS THIRSTY FOR CRAB! WITH MY MOTHER'S HELP I FOUND I ALSO COULD RECREATE DISHES FROM MEMORY JUST LIKE MY GRANNY.

AND NOW I MAKE A SCOTTISH CRAB FEAST.

THE MOST IMPORTANT INGREDIENTS: THE BEAUTIFUL RED MONSTERS SWIMMING AROUND THE SALTY SHORES OF SCOTLAND.

AVGOLEMONO GREEK SCOTCH BROTH (SERVES 4-6)

BY YASMINE SEFRAOUI

INGREDIENTS:

800g LAMB NECK OR SHANK

2L OF WATER

150g CARROTS, DICED

150g ONIONS, DICED

150g CHARD OR SPINACH

150g CELERY, DICED

75g GREEN PEAS

3 GARLIC CLOVES, SLICED

50g PEARL BARLEY

2 BAY LEAVES

2 TABLESPOONS OF DRIED THYME

FRESH PARSLEY TO TASTE

200ml OLIVE OIL

THE ZEST AND JUICE OF 1/2 A LEMON

1 EGG, 2 EGG YOLKS

SALT   PEPPER

PLACE A LARGE HEAVY BOTTOMED PAN ON MEDIUM HEAT, ADD THE OIL.

THEN SWEAT THE ONIONS, CELERY, CARROTS, GARLIC AND LEMON ZEST UNTIL SOFT AND FRAGRANT. (5-10 MINUTES).

ADD THE LAMB AND BAY LEAVES, COVER WITH WATER.

SEASON WITH SALT AND PEPPER.

BRING TO A GENTLE SIMMER, COVER AND COOK FOR ABOUT AN HOUR, SKIMMING THE SURFACE OF THE POT FROM TIME TO TIME TO REMOVE THE SCUM.

AFTER AN HOUR, CAREFULLY REMOVE THE PIECE OF LAMB FROM THE POT AND LET COOL ON A PLATE.

STIR THE BARLEY INTO THE POT, AND SIMMER AGAIN.

ONCE THE LAMB IS COOL ENOUGH TO HANDLE, REMOVE THE MEAT FROM THE BONES AND ROUGHLY CHOP.

ADD THE FLAKED MEAT BACK INTO THE BROTH, AND KEEP SIMMERING UNTIL THE BARLEY IS TENDER.

ONCE THE BARLEY IS COOKED, IT'S TIME TO MAKE THE AVGOLEMONO MIXTURE. IN A MIXING BOWL, WHISK THE EGGS AND LEMON JUICE AND ADD THE THYME.

YOU WANT TO TEMPER THE EGG MIXTURE BY ADDING ABOUT 3 LADLES OF HOT BROTH TO THE EGGS AND WHISKING QUICKLY.

THIS WILL BRING THE TEMPERATURE OF THE EGGS UP AND PREVENT THEM FROM CURDLING WHEN ADDED TO THE SOUP.

LOWER THE HEAT AND ADD THE AVGOLEMONO TO THE POT, STIRRING WELL.

THEN ADD THE PEAS AND CHARD OR SPINACH, COVER AND COOK FOR 5 MINUTES.

TURN OFF THE HEAT AND LET SIT FOR ANOTHER 5 MINUTES. NOW THE SOUP IS READY! SERVE WITH CHOPPED PARSLEY!

LAST NIGHT I DREAMT I WAS MAKING MOLOKHIA

STORY BY SARA SHAARAWI

We cook just the leaves. We dry and mince them.

You melt the ghee first. Samna.

Yes, samna, ghee, you sauté the garlic, you want it to be very fragant.

Add the coriander or cumin and let it cook a bit more. Heat your chicken broth and add the molokhia. Bring it to a boil and add the garlic mixture. Cook until it's the right consistency.

Slimy and thick, something between a stew and a soup. It puts off foreigners.

Serve with white rice and roast chicken. Or rabbit!

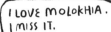

I LOVE MOLOKHIA. I MISS IT.

YOU DON'T HAVE MOLOKHIA IN SCOTLAND?

NO. YOU CAN'T FIND A LOT OF EGYPTIAN FOOD IN SCOTLAND. AND I NEVER LEARNED HOW TO MAKE IT.

WHY NOT?

I GREW UP WITH AN ITALIAN MOTHER.

WHAT DID SHE TEACH YOU?

LASAGNE, RISOTTO, SPEZZATINO & POLENTA, CARBONARA, PARMIGIANA,

HOW DID SHE TEACH YOU?

SHE WROTE DOWN THE RECIPES IN EMAILS. EVERYTHING IS MEASURED BY HAND OR BY EYE OR BY INSTINCT. THAT'S WHY ALL THE RECIPES TASTE SLIGHTLY DIFFERENT. THEY ADAPT TO OUR BODIES, THE SIZE OF OUR PALMS, THE LENGTH OF OUR ATTENTION SPAN, THE APPEAL TO OUR SENSES.

WHAT DO YOU MISS MOST?

KOSHARI, BALADI BREAD, FETEER, TAAMEYA, WARA' 3ENAB. I MISS THE SPREAD OF DISHES ON THE TABLE, SO THAT YOU EAT A BIT OF EVERYTHING. I MISS THE SWEETS. I MISS THE FRUIT.

AND MOLOKHIA IS YOUR FAVOURITE?

IT'S EVERY EGYPTIAN CHILD'S FAVOURITE.

WHERE ARE YOU NOW?

I'M 10 AND I AM EXCITED BECAUSE IT'S SUMMER. SUMMER MEANS MANGOES IN EGYPT AND CHERRIES IN ITALY.

WHERE ARE YOU NOW?

I'M 21 AND EVERYONE IS IN TAHRIR SQUARE. I'M NOT THERE. MY FATHER HAS ASKED ME TO EXPLAIN WHAT I WAS WILLING TO DIE FOR AND I COULDN'T ANSWER.

INSTEAD I WATCH HIM FILL BUCKETS AND BOTTLES WITH TAP WATER, I HELP HIM TAKE TINS OF FOOD, SACKS OF RICE AND BOTTLED WATER TO THE DINING ROOM.

THE POLICE HAVE EVACUATED THE CITY AND WE DON'T KNOW WHAT THE GOVERNMENT MIGHT DO NEXT. THE NEXT DAY, I GO TO TAHRIR WITH MY FATHER.

WHERE ARE YOU NOW?

I'M 27 AND I'VE JUST EXPERIENCED MY FIRST EVER BURNS NIGHT SUPPER. THE NIGHT STARTS OFF WITH THE ODE TO THE HAGGIS, NEEPS AND TATTIES. WE DRINK WHISKY AND EVERYONE SHARES A POEM, SONG OR STORY.

AROUND 2AM, I FEEL HUNGRY AGAIN, I START EATING THE LEFTOVER HAGGIS, AND IN THAT MOMENT I REALISE I AM IN LOVE WITH SCOTLAND.

WHERE ARE YOU NOW?

I AM 18 AND MY MOTHER TRIES TO MAKE MOLOKHIA FOR THE FIRST TIME. IT TASTES A BIT ... NOT RIGHT. SHE'LL KEEP TRYING FOR YEARS.

NOW, WHEN I VISIT, SHE PRESENTS ME WITH A PLATE, AND PROUDLY SAYS: "IT TASTES LIKE AN EGYPTIAN ONE, RIGHT?"

BAKLAVA PANCAKES

(SERVES 4-6)
BY YASMINE SEFRAOUI

INGREDIENTS:

  350g OF SELF-RAISING FLOUR

 2 tsp of BAKING POWDER

 80g (1/3 cup) OF CASTER SUGAR

 2 tsp OF ORANGE BLOSSOM WATER

 AND OR THE FINELY GRATED ZEST OF 1 SMALL ORANGE

2 LARGE EGGS (OR 3 SMALL)

 200ml MILK (3/4 cups)

 VEGETABLE OIL FOR FRYING

FOR TOPPINGS:

 340g HONEY

 115g BUTTER

 120g NUTS (WALNUTS, ALMONDS, PISTACHIOS, OR A COMBINATION OF THEM)

 1 tsp OF CINNAMON

 KAYMAK (TURKISH CLOTTED CREAM) IF YOU CAN'T FIND ANY, REGULAR CLOTTED CREAM

COMBINE THE SELF-RAISING FLOUR, BAKING POWDER, SUGAR AND ORANGE ZEST IN A LARGE MIXING BOWL. MIX THOROUGHLY AND MAKE A WELL IN THE CENTRE.

ADD THE EGG AND ORANGE BLOSSOM WATER AND START BEATING WITH A WHISK WHILE GRADUALLY ADDING THE MILK. THE BATTER SHOULD BE SMOOTH AND CREAMY.

IN A NON-STICK FRYING PAN. HEAT A LITTLE OIL OVER HIGH HEAT. WHEN THE PAN IS HOT, DROP SPOONFULS OF BATTER ON IT. BE CAREFUL TO LEAVE ENOUGH SPACE FOR THE PANCAKES TO SPREAD.

COOK FOR ABOUT 2 MINUTES OR UNTIL BUBBLES APPEAR ON THE SURFACE AND THEN FLIP OVER WITH A SPATULA.

COOK THE OTHER SIDE FOR ANOTHER 30 OR 60 SECONDS. BOTH SIDES SHOULD BE GOLDEN BROWN. ADJUST THE HEAT ACCORDINGLY AND ADD OIL ON THE PAN IF NEEDED.

COVER THE PANCAKES WITH A CLEAN TEA TOWEL TO KEEP THEM WARM. YOU CAN KEEP THEM IN A PREHEATED OVEN IF YOU'D LIKE.

IN A SMALL POT MELT THE BUTTER AND HONEY TOGETHER UNTIL WARM AND FRAGRANT.

CHOP THE NUTS IN A FOOD PROCESSOR OR ALTERNATIVELY BY HAND. THEY SHOULD NEITHER BE TOO COARSELY OR TOO FINELY CHOPPED. MIX IN THE CINNAMON.

ARRANGE THE PANCAKES ON A PLATE, TOP WITH NUTS AND HONEY SYRUP. YOU CAN SERVE THEM PILED UP IF YOU WANT TO CREATE BAKLAVA LIKE LAYERS.

SERVE WITH A GENEROUS DOLLOP OF KAYMAK AND SOME MORE HONEY SYRUP.

THEY'RE READY TO EAT!

THE STATE RECIPE

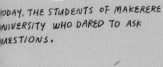

STORY BY
ASIIMWE
DEBORAH
KAWE

ODAY, THE STUDENTS OF MAKERERE NIVERSITY WHO DARED TO ASK UESTIONS,

WHO WALKED THE STREETS OF THEIR CAMPUS TO DEMAND AN EXPLANATION WHY THEIR TUITION WAS RAISED BY 15%,

AND WHO DARED TO ASK ABOUT THEIR RIGHTS AND CIVIL LIBERTIES,

WERE FED ON A FULL DAY OF MEALS PREPARED FOR HEM BY CHEFS CAREFULLY SELECTED BY THE STATE.

THE CHEFS WERE OF HIGH RANK AND MIGHTILY REVERED ACROSS THE COUNTRY.

THEY INCLUDED OFFICERS FROM THE NATIONAL POLICE,

THE MILITARY POLICE. — THEY ARE WELL KNOWN FOR CREATING RECIPES WITH AN EVERLASTING EFFECT!

AND THE VERY MODEST ONES WHO WOULD RATHER NOT SHOW THE NATION WHO THEY REALLY ARE BY CHOOSING NOT TO WEAR THEIR ROYAL REGALIA APRONS, HATS OR AS WE CALL THEM HELMETS.

VERY EARLY IN THE MORNING, THE STUDENTS GATHERED IN SMALL GROUPS CARRYING TREE BRANCHES, WEARING THEIR UNDERGRADUATE RED GOWNS AND CHANTING 'FEES MUST FALL'.

ALREADY THE CHEFS WERE IN THE KITCHEN PUTTING TOGETHER A RECIPE FOR THE STUDENTS' BREAKFAST MENU.

THE RECIPES WERE GOING TO BE SUFFICIENT FOR ALL THE THREE MEALS OF THE DAY.

IF NEED BE, THERE WAS PROVISION FOR MID-MORNING TEA AND AFTER-NOON TEA. OF COURSE, ACCOMPANIED BY SNACKS.

THE CHEFS WERE ALREADY DRESSED FOR THE JOB. THEIR APRONS WERE OF SUCH HIGH QUALITY THAT NOT NO FOOD COULD STAIN THEM, NOT EVEN TOMATO PUREE OR KETCHUP.

THEIR HELMETS AND UNIFORMS HAD UNIQUE DESIGNS, AND EACH SIGNIFIED HOW MANY RECIPES THEY HAD MASTERED AS MOST OF THEM WERE EXPERTS AT PUTTING TOGETHER THESE KIND OF MEALS.

THIS BEING ONE OF THE BEST UNIVERSITIES IN THE COUNTRY WHERE THE STUDENTS TENDED TO CONSUME MORE THAN THEY ARE OFFERED, AND HAVE THE AUDACITY TO DEMAND EVEN MORE, THE CHEFS HAD TO GET GREAT QUANTITIES OF THE BEST INGREDIENTS TO PREPARE THE MEALS.

BY THE TIME THE STUDENTS
STARTED THEIR 'NUE NUE'
CHANT, EVERYTHING WAS
IN PLACE AND THE CHEFS
WERE READY.

WHY WOULDN'T THEY BE? THEY HAD RECEIVED
TRAINING FROM THE BEST IN THE LAND,
AND THERE WAS NO ROOM FOR ANY DOUBTS.

THIS WAS THEIR JOB. THEIR WORK.
THEIR CALLING.

THE STUDENTS HAD NO IDEA WHAT KIND OF
BREAKFAST MENU AWAITED THEM.

THEY THOUGHT IT WOULD BE WHAT THEY USUALLY GOT
WHENEVER THE CHEFS VISITED.

BUT THIS TIME,
THE CHEFS HAD
TAKEN IT A
NOTCH HIGHER
AND WERE READY
TO FOLLOW THE
STUDENTS TO
THEIR HALLS OF
RESIDENCE

AND FEED THEM
SOME EXTRA FOOD
PREPARED JUST
FOR THEM.

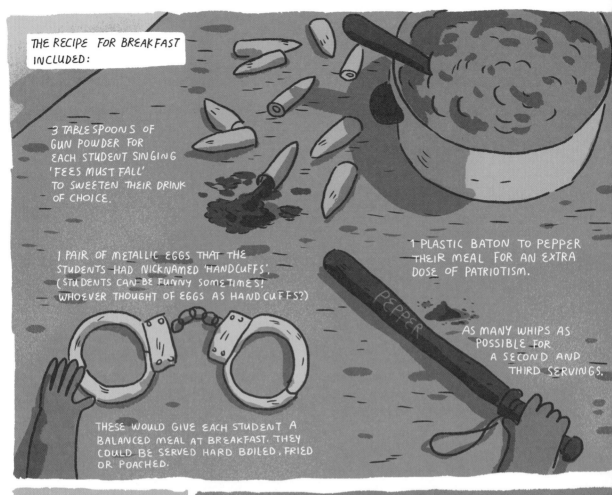

THE RECIPE FOR BREAKFAST INCLUDED:

3 TABLESPOONS OF GUN POWDER FOR EACH STUDENT SINGING 'FEES MUST FALL' TO SWEETEN THEIR DRINK OF CHOICE.

1 PAIR OF METALLIC EGGS THAT THE STUDENTS HAD NICKNAMED 'HANDCUFFS', (STUDENTS CAN BE FUNNY SOMETIMES! WHOEVER THOUGHT OF EGGS AS HANDCUFFS?)

1 PLASTIC BATON TO PEPPER THEIR MEAL FOR AN EXTRA DOSE OF PATRIOTISM.

PEPPER

AS MANY WHIPS AS POSSIBLE FOR A SECOND AND THIRD SERVINGS.

THESE WOULD GIVE EACH STUDENT A BALANCED MEAL AT BREAKFAST. THEY COULD BE SERVED HARD BOILED, FRIED OR POACHED.

THE MORNING TURNED INTO MID-MORNING,

THE STUDENTS DID NOT SEEM TO APPRECIATE THE SUMPTUOUS MEAL THEIR BREAKFAST HAD BEEN.

SO THE CHEFS HAD TO CONSULT WITH THE POWERS FROM ABOVE ABOUT HOW TO MAKE THE STUDENTS EAT MORE FOOD AND APPRECIATE THE CHEFS' WORK.

THE LUNCH PREPERATION HAD TO BE REVISED.

USING THE RECIPE ABOVE AND MORE, ON THE LUNCH MENU THE CHEFS INCLUDED:

BBQ OF HIGHLY SPICED PEPPER SPRAY

ANY CHOICE OF SALAD WITH TEAR GAS DRESSING

FOR DESSERT, THE STUDENTS WERE SERVED SCARLET ICE CREAM.

THERE WILL ALWAYS BE PEOPLE WHO DON'T APPRECIATE THE KIND OF WORK THAT GOES INTO THESE RECIPES AND THE EMOTIONAL ENERGY IT TAKES FOR CHEFS TO CARRY OUT THESE KINDS OF LUNCH ORDERS.

JUST LIKE ANYONE WOULD GET FRUSTRATED WHEN THEIR WORK IS NOT BEING APPRECIATED, THESE CHEFS FELT UNAPPRECIATED BY THE STUDENTS.

AS THE AFTERNOON TURNED INTO EVENING, THE CHEFS TRIED TO FIGURE OUT HOW TO MAKE THE STUDENTS APPRECIATE THE WORK THEY WERE DOING.

THE CHEFS HAD TO THINK HARDER ABOUT HOW TO MAKE THE STUDENTS' SUPPER A MEAL TO REMEMBER.

THE CHEFS BROUGHT IN MORE EQUIPMENT TO PREPARE THE STUDENTS' SUPPER, INCLUDING:

ARMOURED VEHICLES TO MAKE THE MEAL PREPARATION FASTER IN CASE THE STUDENTS STARTED DEMANDING FOR FOOD BEFORE IT WAS READY.

THE CHEFS ALSO INCLUDED AN APPETIZER OF SPICED RUBBER BULLETS.

AND THE MAIN COURSE WAS SIZZLING FURY LIVE BULLETS.

THE DESSERT WAS A SCARLET CAKE TO MATCH THE STUDENTS' UNDERGRADUATE GOWNS.

WHAT THE CHEFS DIDN'T EXPECT WAS THE FACT THAT SOME STUDENTS STILL DIDN'T APPRECIATE THE SUPPER THAT WAS SERVED THEM.

THE CHEFS TOOK IT UPON THEMSELVES TO FOLLOW THE STUDENTS TO THEIR HALLS OF RESIDENCE WHERE THEY HA[D] ALL RETREATED AND DECIDED TO FEED THEM THERE.

METALLIC DOORS CAME DOWN, DOORS LEADING TO THE STUDENTS' DORMS WERE TORN OPEN.

IN THE WOMEN'S HALLS OF RESIDENCE, FEMALE STUDENTS WERE TAUGHT HOW TO RESPECT THEIR ELDERS, IN WAYS THAT ARE WAY HARDER TO WRITE ABOUT.

SOME OF THE FEMALE STUDENTS ARE STILL IN HIDING TODAY BECAUSE THE MEALS THEY WERE SERVED IN THE HALLS OF RESIDENCE THAT DAY HAD NO WITNESSES.

THE SHAME, THE HUMILIATION, THE TRAUMA THAT CAME WITH WHAT THEY WERE FED THAT DAY. IT NEVER GOES AWAY.

AFTER THE CHEFS WERE CONVINCED THAT THE STUDENTS' MEAL WAS SATISFACTORY, THEY LEFT THE UNIVERSITY CAMPUS.

THEY PATTED THEMSELVES ON THE BACK FOR THE SERVICE THEY HAD RENDERED THE NATION.

IT WAS JUST ANOTHER DAY, AND THEY KNEW THAT THEY WOULD BE CALLED ON AGAIN SOON TO PREPARE ANOTHER MEAL FOR ANOTHER GROUP OF CITIZENS SINGING UNWANTED SONGS.

AND THE STATE RECIPE CONTINUES...

PERSIAN AUBERGINE AND BARLEY PORRIDGE

SERVES 4-6

BY YASMINE SEFRAOUI

INGREDIENTS

PEARL BARLEY

400gm (2 cups)

WATER

1L (4 CUPS)

OR CHICKEN / VEGETABLE STOCK

1 GENEROUS PINCH OF SAFFRON

3 MEDIUM ONIONS,

3 GARLIC CLOVES

2 MEDIUM AUBERGINES

125 gm (1 CUP) OF WALNUTS

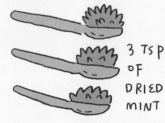

3 TSP OF DRIED MINT

LABNEH OR GREEK YOGHURT TO TASTE

POMEGRANATE

1 KNOB OF BUTTER

SALT

PEPPER

START BY SEEDING THE POMEGRANATE AND ROUGHLY CHOPPING THE WALNUTS THEN SET BOTH ASIDE.

IN A POT BRING THE WATER OR STOCK TO A BOIL. ADD THE PINCH OF SAFFRON AND THE BARLEY AND SIMMER UNTIL SOFT (30-35 MINS).

WHILE THE BARLEY COOKS, THINLY SLICE THE ONIONS, CHOP GARLIC AND CUT THE AUBERGINE INTO 1 INCH THICK CHUNKS.

PLACE THE AUBERGINE CHUNKS IN A COLANDER. GENEROUSLY SALT THEM AND LET THEM SIT.

ADD SOME VEGETABLE OIL TO A FRYING PAN AND FRY THE ONIONS UNTIL CRISPY AND GOLDEN BROW. SEASON WITH SALT AND SET ASIDE. USING THE SAME PAN, FRY GARLIC AND SET ASIDE.

RINSE THE AUBERGINE AND PAT DRY. ADD A GENEROUS AMOUNT OF OIL TO THE PAN AND FRY THEM ON MEDIUM HEAT UNTIL CRISP ON THE OUTSIDE AND SOFT INSIDE. SEASON AND SET ASIDE.

FRY THE MINT.

ONCE COOKED, DRAIN THE BARLEY AND RETURN IT TO THE POT. ADD A KNOB OF BUTTER AND INCORPORATE HALF OF THE CRISPY ONIONS, THE FRIED GARLIC, AND HALF OF THE FRIED MINT, SALT AND PEPPER TO TASTE.

PLACE THE BARLEY IN A BOWL AND TOP IT WITH A GENEROUS DOLLOP OF LABNEH OR YOGHURT. THE AUBERGINE, THE REST OF THE CRISPY ONIONS, AND THE MINT. SCATTER WITH THE CHOPPED WALNUTS AND POMEGRANATE SEEDS.

45

BANYARWANDA

POEM BY
ERY NZARAMBA

SOME PLACES HAVE

ANTIQUITY

MIDDLE AGES

MODERN TIMES

OTHER PLACES HAVE

PRE-COLONIALISM

OST-COLONIALISM

SUPERMARKET   SALE

BANANAS

HEY DIDN'T HAVE BANANAS IN THE
IIDDLE AGES

THEY'D STAYED IN THE MIDDLE
IF ONLY THEY'D MIGRATED

IT WOULD NOT HAVE
TAKEN THEM AGES

TO FIND
BANANAS
IN AFRICA

THE CONTINENT
OF
GREEN, RED
AND YELLOW

I CAME FROM A COUNTRY
IN THE MIDDLE OF AFRICA
CALLED A 'BANANA REPUBLIC'
 FOR AGES
DURING MOST OF
 POST-COLONIALISM

YET DURING
ANTIQUITY

MIDDLE AGES

PRE-COLONIALISM

POST-COLONIALISM

MODERN TIMES

IT'S ALWAYS BEEN
 A REPUBLIC OF BANANAS

WHERE THE BANANA REIGNS

BANANA!
YOU'RE THE FRUIT THAT BEARS
THE AFRICAN COLOURS!

WHEN YOU'RE GREEN
THE COLOUR OF OUR THOUSAND ROLLING HILLS

WE CALL YOU BITOKE
AND YOU GIVE US OUR NATIONAL DISH

WHEN YOU'RE YELLOW
THE COLOUR OF
OUR EVERLASTING
SUN
WE CALL YOU MUNEKE

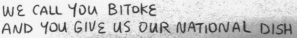

AND YOU GIVE US OUR
NATIONAL DRINK:
URWAGWA FOR THE OLD
UMUTOBE FOR THE YOUNG

HEN YOU'RE RED
HE COLOUR OF
OUR DEEP RICH SOIL

SO RICH IT HURTS

YOU'VE ROTTED
YOU'VE GONE RED
WE'VE LET YOU DOWN

GREEN ENERGY

YELLOW LIFE

RED BLOOD

OH GOD. I'M GOING BANANAS!

... SO WE MIGRATE ...

MAQLOUBA

STORY BY
LUBNA
SAID
ALHAJJAR

'MAQLOUBA' MEANS 'UPSIDE DOWN' IN MY LANGUAGE ARABIC.

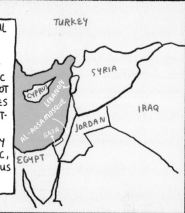

IT IS OUR TRADITIONAL DISH, BOTH HERE IN PALESTINE BUT ALSO ACROSS THE LEVANT - A LARGE GEOGRAPHIC AREA WHICH DOES NOT HAVE FIXED BOUNDARIES OR BORDERS BUT INSTEAD AN IDENTITY, A BENDING BOUNDARY OF FAMILIAR LINGUISTIC, CULTURAL AND RELIGIOUS TRAITS.

TURKEY
SYRIA
CYPRUS
LEBANON
AL-AQSA MOSQUE
IRAQ
GAZA
JORDAN
EGYPT

THE ANCIENT HISTORY OF THE LEVANT INCLUDES THE AKKADIAN EMPIRE, AMORITE KINGDOM, HITTITE KINGDOM, ASSYRIANS, PERSIANS, GREEKS, SELEUCIDS, BYZANTINES, ARABS,

AND MORE ...

THAT'S A LOT OF HISTORY! SO MANY EMPIRES AND WARS. AND STILL SO MANY WARS TODAY AND TOMORROW. OUCH, IT MAKES MY BRAIN HURT!

AUBERGINE IS MY FAVOURITE INGREDIENT, AND MAQLOUBA MY FAVOURITE DISH. MAQLOUBA IS MADE-UP OF MEAT, VEGETABLE AND RICE LAYERS COOKED IN A **BIG** POT.

THE SECRET TO ALL COOKING, MY MOTHER SAYS, IS THE MAKING AND MIXING OF SPICES!

FIRST YOU MUST MIX ALL THE GROUND SPICES IN A BOWL, THAT'S 1½ TEASPOONS OF TURMERIC.

1 TEASPOON GROUND GINGER, CINNAMON, ALLSPICE.

½ TEASPOON OF GROUND CARDAMOM, CLOVES AND BLACK PEPPER. PUT SPICE MIX ASIDE.

NEXT, PREPARE THE BROTH. ROUGHLY CHOP 2 ONIONS, HEAT 2 TEASPOONS OF VEGETABLE OIL IN A LARGE SAUCEPAN AND FRY.

IF YOU DECIDE TO USE A WHOLE CHICKEN, CUT IT UP INTO PIECES. ADD THEM TO THE SAUCEPAN AND FRY EVENLY ON EACH SIDE FOR 5 MINUTES.

WHEN THE CHICKEN HAS SOME COLOUR, POUR ABOUT 2 LITRES OF WATER IN THE PAN, ENSURING THE CHICKEN IS COMPLETELY COVERED.

THROW IN 4 BAY LEAVES, 1 HEAPED TEASPOON OF SALT AND 1 HEAPED TEASPOON OF THE SPICE MIX,

BRING TO BOIL THEN COVER WITH THE LID AND LET IT SIMMER ON MEDIUM HEAT FOR 45 MINUTES.

AS IT COOKS, SOME FOAM MIGHT FORM ON THE SURFACE OF THE WATER, IT'S BEST TO REMOVE IT WITH A SPOON SO KEEP CHECKING AS IT BOILS.

MAQLOUBA CELEBRATES THE VICTORY OF COMMANDER SALAH ELDEN AL-AYOUBI AND HIS SOLDIERS AGAINST EUROPEAN CRUSADERS, WHERE THE COMMANDER AND HIS SOLDIERS REGAINED CONTROL OVER AL-QUDS (JERUSALEM). A VICTORY WHICH ALLOWED MUSLIMS TO PRAY AT THE AL-AQSA MOSQUE ONCE AGAIN.

THE PALESTINIANS PRESENTED MAQLOUBA TO HIM, WHICH HE LIKED VERY MUCH, DESCRIBING IT AS AN 'UPSIDE DOWN' CAKE.

NOW, FOR PREPARING THE VEGETABLES,' MY MUM SAYS

PEEL 2 AUBERGINES, 2 CARROTS, 2 MEDIUM ONIONS AND 2 POTATOES AND CUT INTO THICK SLICES.

IN A FRYING PAN, HEAT A GENEROUS QUANTITY OF VEGETABLE OIL - ABOUT 1CM DEEP. FRY ALL VEGETABLES IN SMALL BATCHES UNTIL GOLDEN BROWN ON EACH SIDE.

L-AQSA MOSQUE IS WHERE MU-AMMAD (PEACE BE UPON HIM) ETHERED BURAQ TO THE AL-BURAQ ALL AND PRAYED. AFTER HE FI-ISHED HIS PRAYERS HE ASCEN-ED TO HEAVEN AND SPOKE TO GOD. IS ASCENT INTO THE HEAVENS KNOWN AS THE 'MI RAJ'.

HEAT 50ML OF OLIVE OIL IN A POT. DD 500g OF RICE AND COOK AT LOW HEAT FOR AROUND 7 MINU-ES - STIR CONTINUOUSLY AS WELL S SPRINKLING IN THE REMAINING PICE MIX. THE SPICED RICE IS MAQLOUBA'S LAST LAYER.

ONCE THE CHICKEN IS COOKED, TAKE THE PIECES OUT OF THE BROTH AND PUT ASIDE.

POUR THE BROTH THROUGH A SIEVE INTO A SEPERATE BOWL SO YOU KEEP ONLY THE LIQUID.

OW FOR ASSEMBLING THE MAQLOUBA, Y DOWN THE CHICKEN THEN THE EGETABLES, AND FINALLY SPREAD THE ICE OVER THEM, MAKING 3 EVEN LAY-RS, SO LATER WHEN THE POT GETS FLIP-ED FOR SERVING, THE DISH LOOKS LIKE LAYERED CAKE.

PLACE A SMALL PLATE ON TOP OF THE LAYERED DISH TO KEEP EVERYTHING IN PLACE WHILE IT COOKS.

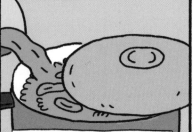

NOW POUR THE BROTH IN THE PAN UNTIL IT REACHES THE SAME LEVEL AS THE RICE OR JUST ABOVE IT (YOU WILL NEED ABOUT 700/800 ML OF BROTH).

53

BRING TO BOIL, COVER AND LET IT SIMMER ON MEDIUM HEAT FOR ABOUT 20 MINUTES OR UNTIL THERE IS ABSOLUTELY NO LIQUID LEFT.

THEN TAKE IT OFF THE HEAT AND LEAVE TO REST FOR 15 MINUTES WITH THE LID ON.

MAQLOUBA IS OFTEN EATEN ON FRIDAYS – THE ISLAMIC DAY OF WORSHIP. YOU MUST WAIT TO FLIP IT UNTIL ALL GUESTS AND FAMILY MEMBERS HAVE GATHERED – TO SEE THE SHAPE, LAYERS AND SMELLS OF THIS YUMMY CAKE.

THE DREAM IS TO EAT MAQLOUBA IN THE GARDEN OF AL-AQSA MOSQUE.

NOWADAYS, MANY PALESTINIANS ARE ATTACKED WITH TEAR GAS, RUBBER BULLETS AND SOUND GRENADES BY THE ISRAELI FORCES TO PREVENT THEM FROM PRAYING AT AL-AQSA MOSQUE IN AL-QUDS OR HAVING MAQLOUBA IN ITS GARDEN.

A WAY FOR US TO CHALLENGE AND EXPRESS RESISTANCE IS FOR PALESTINIANS TO PRAY AND PREPARE MAQLOUBA AT THE BORDERS OF AL-AQSA MOSQUE AND GARDEN, SHARING OUR RICH HISTORY AND EXPRESSING LIFE LIVING UNDER SIEGE.

EVERYWHERE IN MY HOUSE I SEE AL-AQSA MOSQUE.

WE EVEN HAVE AL-AQSA IN 3D.

I LIVE IN GAZA, PALESTINE – A STRIP OF LAND WHICH IS ONLY 41 KM LONG. I LIVE WITH AROUND 1.85 MILLION OTHER PALESTINIANS UNDER ISRAELI SIEGE. I CANNOT LEAVE THIS STRIP OF LAND.

NOW FOR THE FLIPPING AND EATING OF OUR MAQLOUBA. OPEN THE PAN AND REMOVE THE SMALL PLATE. PUT A LARGE TRAY OR PLATE OVER THE PAN.

HOLD IT TIGHT AND FLIP IT OVER SO THE MAQLOUBA TRANSFERS ON TO THE PLATE.

MY MUM LIKES SO SPRINKLE SOME ROASTED ALMONDS, PEANUTS OR PINENUTS, WITH FRESH PARSLEY OVER THE TOP.

WE EAT IT WITH SALAD AND FRESH YOGHURT.

AND WE EAT IT IN FRONT OF AL-ASQA MOSQUE.

ONE DAY I WILL SEE MY LAND. AND I WILL PREPARE MAQLOUBA AND WE WILL EAT IT IN THE GARDEN OF AL-AQSA MOSQUE. 'INSHALLAH.'

NEEPS GOBI

SERVES 4

BY SAUBIA SAFDAR
AND KIRSTY GIBSON

I LARGE NEEP. CUBED.

1 MEDIUM CAULIFLOWER CUT INTO SMALL FLORETS

1 ONION, CHOPPED.

2 TOMATOES. CHOPPED.

1/2 TSP CUMIN SEEDS

1 1/2 TSP GINGER-GARLIC PASTE

1/2 TSP TURMERIC POWDER

1/2 TSP CHILLI POWDER

1/2 TSP GARAM MASALA POWDER

1 TSP CORIANDER POWDER

3-4 TSP VEGETABLE OIL

20g FRESH CORIANDER CHOPPED

SALT AND PEPPER

FRY THE CAULIFLOWER TIL IT IS HALF COOKED.

PARBOIL THE NEEPS THEN FRY UNTIL PAR COOKED, ENSURING IT RETAINS SHAPE AND TEXTURE.

HEAT OILED PAN. ADD CUMIN SEEDS AND LET THEM CRACKLE. ONCE FRAGRANT, ADD ONIONS AND COOK UNTIL SOFT.

ADD THE GINGER-GARLIC PASTE AND COOK FOR 2 MINUTES, THEN ADD THE CHOPPED TOMATOES AND COOK UNTIL SOFT.

ADD TURMERIC, CHILLI AND CORIANDER POWDER, COVER AND ALLOW TO COOK FOR 2-3 MINUTES, THEN ADD THE CAULIFLOWER AND NEEPS.

STIR IN THE CHOPPED CORIANDER LEAVES, ADD THE GARAM MASALA. LET THE NEEPS AND CAULIFLOWER COOK ON MEDIUM-LOW HEAT FOR A FURTHER 5-6 MINUTES.

ADD SALT AND PEPPER TO TASTE AND CONTINUE TO COOK FOR 6-7 MINUTES ON LOW FLAME OR UNTIL THE NEEPS AND CAULIFLOWER ARE TENDER. IF THE PAN SEEMS TOO DRY, ADD A LITTLE WATER TO PREVENT STICKING.

THE FLAVOUR OF HOME AWAY FROM HOME

STORY BY SUMAYYA USMANI

FLAVOUR HAS ALWAYS BEEN MY FIRST CONNECTION TO A PLACE. AND EXPLORING FOOD IN A NEW COUNTRY HAS HELPED ME FIND MY PLACE WITHIN IT.

RESTAURANT

CITY MAP

I FIND A SUBTLE SENSE OF FAMILIARITY IN SCOTLAND. LIKE PAKISTAN, IT HAS DRAMATIC SCENERY, HOSPITABLE PEOPLE AND A HISTORY OF INVASIONS AND MIGRATION THAT HAVE MARKED ITS CULTURE AND CUISINE.

SCOTTISH FOOD IS MUCH MORE THAN HAGGIS AND SHORT BREAD – JUST LIKE PAKISTANI CUISINE, IT IS DEFINED BY SEASONALITY AND PRODUCE.

WITH NEW INGREDIENTS AROUND ME, I'VE BEGUN TO SUBSTITUTE AND EXPERIMENT WITH CLASSIC PAKISTANI RECIPES, IN ORDER TO MAKE A HOME AWAY FROM HOME.

ONE OF THE FIRST CULINARY SIMIL-ARITIES THAT STRUCK ME WAS THE LOVE FOR SLOW COOKED MEATS IN SCOTLAND.

IN PAKISTAN, WE EAT A LOT OF MUTTON, GOAT AND BEEF, WHICH IS EITHER SLOW-COOKED, STIR-FRIED OR BARBECUED WITH SPICES OR SIMPLY WITH ANIMAL FAT AND HERBS, DEPENDING ON WHERE YOU ARE.

THERE'S A SIMILAR LOVE FOR SLOW-COOKED STEWS IN SCOTLAND, SOMETIMES WITH SIMPLE HERB FLAVOURS SUCH AS JUNIPER, BAY OR THYME.

I LEARNT TO ADAPT MY GRANDMOTHER'S CHUKANDAR GOSHT (BEETROOT AND BEEF CURRY) WITH SCOTTISH VENISON AND JUNIPER MIXED WITH STAR ANISE.

DARK SPICES, SUCH AS SMOKEY BLACK CARDAMOM, PEPPER-CORNS AND STAR ANISE ADD A DARK DEPTH OF FLAVOUR SIMILAR TO MANY PAKISTANI DISHES.

THIS RECIPE CELEBRATES THE SCOTTISH AND PAKI-STANI LOVE FOR SHARING SINGLE-POT MEALS. IN SCOTLAND IT CAN BE BROTH OR STEWS, IN PAKISTAN IT CAN BE BIRYANI, MIHARI OR HALEEM (MEAT AND OAT PORRIDGE).

MOVED TO SCOTLAND IN THE SUMMER, AND MY FIRST TASTE OF A SCOTTISH RASPBERRY IS AN EXPERIENCE I WON'T FORGET SOON.

THE INTENSE VIOLET FLAVOUR HEIGHTENED BY SOUGHT AFTER SUN-SHINE.

THE FRAGRANCE AND FLAVOUR OF SCOTTISH SUMMER RASPBERRIES ARE PERFECT FOR SCOTTISH DESSERT CRANACHAN.

THE TRADITIONAL WAY TO SERVE CRANACHAN IS TO ALLOW YOUR GUESTS TO MAKE UP THEIR OWN DESSERT, SERVING EACH ELEMENT OF THE DISH SEPERATELY.

I COULDN'T RESIST MAKING MY OWN VERSION USING PAKISTAN'S MOST SOUGHT AFTER FRUIT - I USE HUNZA APRICOTS, WHICH FOR ME EVOKE EARLY AUTUMN IN NORTHERN PAKISTAN

HOWEVER, THIS RECIPE I SHARE WITH YOU NOW HAS TO BE THE ONE THAT GIVES ME THE MOST COMFORT.

AS A CHILD, I WOULD WAKE UP ON A SUNDAY MORNING TO BE GREETED BY THE SMOKEY SCENT OF FRESH PARATHAS BEING MADE ON THE TAWA (FLAT GRIDDLE PAN),

MY MOUTH WATERING IN ANTICIPATION OF BREAKFAST.

MY MOTHER MADE THESE BY MIXING LEFTOVER MASHED POTATO BHUJIA (STIR-FRIED POTATO) INTO FLOUR TO MAKE THICK BREADS WITH GENEROUS AMOUNTS OF FRESH CORIANDER, GREEN CHILLI, CUMIN AND GHEE.

WHEN I MOVED TO GLASGOW, I WAS AMAZED AT HOW SIMILAR PARATHAS WERE TO TATTIE SCONES - LEFTOVER MASH MIXED WITH FLOUR AND BUTTER, BEST COOKED ON A CAST IRON 'GIRDLE'.

FOR ME THIS IS MY GO-TO BREAKFAST NOW.

IN MY COOK SCHOOL IN GLASGOW, WE BASE MANY CLASSES ON CONNECTING PEOPLE TO FOOD THROUGH THEIR MEMORIES OF GROWING UP.

AND I HAVE REALISED THAT THIS STORY IS SHARED BY MANY, FOOD DOES FIND YOU HOME NO MATTER WHERE YOU ARE.

MANY OF THE PEOPLE I TEACH ARE FROM DIFFERENT PARTS OF THE WORLD AND IT IS FASCINATING TO FIND THE WAYS TO USE FOOD AND FIND COMFORT AND BELONGING IN A NEW PLACE.

THE WORLD IS FILLED WITH MANY DIFFERENT PEOPLE, CULTURES AND TRADITIONS — BUT FOOD IS THE CONNECTION THAT WE ALL SHARE AND ONE THAT BRIDGES ALL THE DIFFERENCES.

I'VE REALLY ONLY STARTED TO EXPLORE THE CROSSOVER BETWEEN THESE CUISINES, AND HOW I CAN USE NEW PRODUCE IN MY COOKING.

BUT MY JOURNEY FROM KARACHI TO GLASGOW, I HAVE REALISED I CAN FIND 'HOME' THROUGH FOOD PRODUCE, CULINARY HERITAGE AND FLAVOUR — AND THE JOURNEY HAS ONLY JUST BEGUN.

60g BUTTERNUT SQUASH, ROASTED UNTIL SOFT

I MEDIUM POTATO, PEELED, CHOPPED, BOILED AND MASHED

100g PLAIN FLOUR, PLUS EXTRA FOR DUSTING

1/2 TSP SALT

1/2 TSP GROUND TURMERIC

I TSP CUMIN SEEDS TOASTED

2 TSP CORIANDER, FINELY CHOPPED

6 MINT LEAVES, FINELY CHOPPED

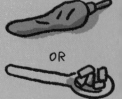

OR

I GREEN CHILLI, FINELY CHOPPED OR 1/2 TSP RED CHILLI FLAKES

2 SPRING ONIONS, FINELY CHOPPED

JUICE OF 1/2 LIME

3-4 TBSP GHEE, OR 3-4 TBSP COCONUT, RAPESEED OR VEGETABLE OIL

SCOTTISTANI SPICED WINTER SQUASH AND 'TATTIE SCONE' PARATHA

SERVES 6–

MIX ALL THE INGREDIENTS TOGETHER (EXCEPT THE GHEE), IN A LARGE BOWL.

STIR IN THE MELTED GHEE, A LITTLE AT A TIME, UNTIL THE MIXTURE REACHES A DOUGH-LIKE CONSISTENCY.

TURN OUT ON TO A FLOURED WORK SURFACE AND KNEAD UNTIL SMOOTH.

DIVIDE THE DOUGH INTO TENNIS BALL-SIZED PIECES. COVER WITH A DAMP CLOTH.

HEAT A GRIDDLE PAN, TAWA OR FRYING PAN OVER A HIGH HEAT.

WHEN HOT, ADD A LITTLE GHEE, THEN REDUCE THE HEAT TO MEDIUM.

ON A FLOURED SURFACE, ROLL EACH DOUGH BALL INTO A 6MM-THICK PATTY.

PLACE IN THE HOT GHEE AND COOK GENTLY, PRESSING DOWN THE CORNERS WITH A CLEAN TEA TOWEL OR KITCHEN PAPER, TO ENSURE IT BROWNS EVENLY.

WHEN ONE SIDE IS COOKED - ABOUT 3-4 MINUTES- TURN OVER AND COOK THE OTHER SIDE. REPEAT WITH THE REMAINING DOUGH.

EN JOY!!

BELLY BUTTON

STORY BY
SHAZIA

WHEN SHAZIA WAS A LITTLE GIRL, HER GRANDMOTHER WOULD TELL HER THIS STORY.

IN ANCIENT TIMES, WE HAD A LID OVER OUR BELLIES. THIS WAS CALLED THE BELLY BUTTON. THE BELLY BUTTON COULD BE OPENED AND CLOSED.

THERE WAS A COUPLE WHO LIVED IN A SMALL VILLAGE. THEY WERE SO POOR THAT THEY NEVER HAD MUCH TO EAT.

ONE DAY, THE HUSBAND WENT TO THE FOREST TO COLLECT SOME WOOD. HIS WIFE STAYED AT HOME.

WHILE THE HUSBAND WAS OUT, THEIR NEIGHBOUR CAME BY AND GAVE THEM SOME MEAT TO EAT.

SHE WAS SO HAPPY TO EAT MEAT BECAUSE THEY HADN'T BEEN ABLE TO AFFORD ANY FOR SUCH A LONG TIME.

SHE COOKED THE FRESH PIECES OF MEAT AND BECAUSE SHE WAS SO HUNGRY, SHE ATE IT ALL UP.

NUMB. THAT CRACKLY FEELING COMES BACK.

LIKE THE ONE IN THE PITCH-DARK, BUT THIS TIME IT'S WITH THE SOUND AROUND ME.

A CRACKLY SILENCE LOUD IN MY EARS. I CAN'T REMEMBER WHAT IT TASTED LIKE.

— END —

CONTRIBUTORS

ANDRÉS BLANCO

YASMINE SEFRAOUI

EMMA BROWN

LUBNA SAID ALHAJJAR

ANDREW FORTEATH 'DESIGNER'

ASIIMWE DEBORAH KAWE

ERY NZARAMBA

SARA SHAARAWI

KATIE CATLING

KERRY HUDSON

KIRSTY GIBSON

ASHUTOSH JHA 'REPLIKA PRESS'

SUMAYYA USMANI

REBECCA TANTONY

DEBORAH MAY 'KÜCHE'

EMILY DEWHURST 'KITCHEN PRESS'

SHAZIA

Yasmine Sefraoui

A cook and researcher of Brazilian, Moroccan , and French heritage, Yasmine's cooking is inspired by multiculturalism and storytelling. Yasmine is interested in the ways encounters, memories, and identities are shaped and celebrated through food.

Kirsty Gibson

Creative Glasgow girl, who's childhood dream was to spin and lasso baddies like Wonder Woman. Still spinning but traded the lasso for cooking utensils. The power of cooking for Kirsty brings joy, comfort, and sharing cultural diversity.

Ery Nzaramba

Ery is a Rwandan storyteller who writes and performs for the universal stage and screen. He's currently based in the UK.

Emma Brown

Emma was born and raised in Glasgow and has always been passionate about bringing people together through the universal love of food and cooking.

Kerry Hudson

Kerry Hudson is a novelist and memoirist. She now cooks the Scottish food she grew up with in her new home, Prague.

Asiimwe Deborah Kawe

Asiimwe Deborah Kawe was born in Kiruhura, in South Western Uganda. She is an award-winning playwright, producer and performer based in Kampala, Uganda. A graduate from Makerere University and California Institute of the Arts.

Katie Catling

Katie is a trained cultural anthropologist and enjoys writing in her spare time. Born and bread in Sheffield, she now calls Amsterdam home.

Rebecca Tantony

Rebecca Tantony is the author of three collections of poetry and flash fiction. She has read her work globally and taught Creative Writing in a variety of institutions including Wits University, Johannesburg and Bath Spa University.

Sumayya Usmani

Sumayya Usmani is an award-winning cookbook author, broadcaster, food educator and author of 'Summers Under the Tamarind Tree' and 'Mountain Berries and Desert Spice'. She is also the Founder of social enterprise cook school 'Kaleyard'.

Sonia Michalewicz

Sonia is a keen advocator of sharing and celebrating the culture and heritage of the Roma people in Scotland. She is both a keen Roma gypsy dancer and cook.

Shazia

Shazia is Pakistani cook, mother and creative currently making home in Glasgow.

Andrés Blanco

Andrés is originally from Venezuela but settled in 'Glesga' with his wife and wee baby girl. He is passionate about cooking, humanity and kindness, electricity and renewable energy.

Lubna Said Alhajjar

Lubna is a Palestinian entrepreneur living in Gaza. She is a determined, creative open-minded and easygoing person who loves making desserts and gardening.

Sara Shaarawi

Sara is a playwright from Egypt but has been based in Glasgow for several years now. Although she misses the heat of the sun, she loves the warmth of the communities here.

FUNDERS